A FIRST
GOLDEN
TREASURY

—— OF ——

CHILDREN'S
VERSE

COMPILED BY MARK DANIEL

M

MACMILLAN CHILDREN'S BOOKS

For Pauline

Conceived by Breslich & Foss

This anthology copyright © Mark Daniel 1986

Design © Breslich & Foss 1986

First published in Great Britain in 1986 by Pavilion Books Limited
in association with Michael Joseph Limited

Premier Picturemac edition published 1989 by
Macmillan Children's Books
A division of Macmillan Publishers Limited
London and Basingstoke
Associated companies throughout the world

ISBN 0-333-51036-4

A CIP catalogue record for this book is available from the British Library

Printed in Hong Kong

All colour pictures are courtesy of
Fine Art Photographic Library, London
Front cover painting by Joseph Kirkpatrick
Back cover painting by Erskine Nicol

CONTENTS

DAYBREAK

TIME TO RISE

A birdie with a yellow bill
Hopped upon the window sill,
Cocked his shining eye and said:
'Ain't you 'shamed, you sleepy-head?

ROBERT LOUIS STEVENSON

A Child's Garden of Verses, 1885

Cocks crow in the morn
To tell us to rise,
And he who lies late
Will never be wise;
For early to bed
And early to rise
Makes a man healthy
And wealthy and wise.

ANON

SLUG-ABED

Get up, get up, you lazyhead,
Get up, you lazy sinner!
We need those sheets for tablecloths –
It's nearly time for dinner!

ANON

Donkey, donkey, old and gray,
Ope your mouth, and gently bray;
Lift your ears and blow your horn,
To wake the world this sleepy morn.

ANON

Cock Robin got up early
At the break of day,
And went to Jenny's window
To sing a roundelay,
He sang Cock Robin's love
To the little Jenny Wren,
And when he got unto the end,
Then he began again.

ANON

THE WIND

Who has seen the wind?
   Neither I nor you;
But when the leaves hang trembling
   The wind is passing through.

Who has seen the wind?
   Neither you nor I;
But when the trees bow down their heads
   The wind is passing by.

CHRISTINA GEORGINA ROSSETTI

Sing-Song, 1872

THE THROSTLE

"Summer is coming, summer is coming,
I know it, I know it, I know it.
Light again, leaf again, love again,"
Yes, my wild little poet.

Sing the new year in under the blue,
Last year you sang it as gladly,
"New, new, new, new!" Is it then *so* new
That you should carol so madly?

"Love again, song again, nest again, young again,"
Never a prophet so crazy!
And hardly a daisy as yet, little friend,
See, there is hardly a daisy.

"Here again, here, here, here, happy year!"
O, warble unchidden, unbidden!
Summer is coming, is coming, my dear,
And all the winters are hidden.

ALFRED, LORD TENNYSON

Demeter and Other Poems, 1889

WEATHERS

This is the weather the cuckoo likes,
      And so do I;
When showers betumble the chestnut spikes,
      And nestlings fly;
And the little brown nightingale bills his best,
And they sit outside the "Traveller's Rest,"
And maids come forth sprig-muslin dressed,
And citizens dream of the South and West.
      And so do I.

This is the weather the shepherd shuns,
      And so do I;
When beeches drip in browns and duns,
      And thresh, and ply;
And hill-hid tides throb, throe on throe,
And meadow rivulets overflow,
And drops on gate-bars hang in a row,
And rooks in families homeward go,
      And so do I.

THOMAS HARDY

Late Lyrics in The Complete Poems, 1922 edition

It's raining, it's pouring,
The old man is snoring;
He went to bed and bumped his head
And couldn't get up in the morning!

ANON

A SWARM OF BEES

A swarm of bees in May
Is worth a load of hay;
A swarm of bees in June
Is worth a silver spoon;
A swarm of bees in July
Is not worth a fly.

ANON

MONDAY'S CHILD

Monday's child is fair of face,
Tuesday's child is full of grace,
Wednesday's child is full of woe,
Thursday's child has far to go,
Friday's child is loving and giving,
Saturday's child works hard for its living,
And a child that's born on the Sabbath day
Is blithe and bonny and good and gay.

ANON

WRITTEN IN MARCH

The cock is crowing,
The stream is flowing,
The small birds twitter,
The lake doth glitter,
The green field sleeps in the sun;
The oldest and the youngest
Are at work with the strongest;
The cattle are grazing,
Their heads never raising;
There are forty feeding as one!

Like an army defeated
The snow hath retreated,
And now doth fare ill
On the top of the bare hill;
The ploughboy is whooping – anon – anon:
There's joy in the mountains;
There's life in the fountains;
Small clouds are sailing,
Blue sky prevailing;
The rain is over and gone!

WILLIAM WORDSWORTH

Poems of the Imagination, 1807

Red sky at night,
Shepherd's delight;
Red sky in the morning,
Shepherd's warning.

ANON

March winds and April showers
Bring forth May flowers.

ANON

Come the oak before the ash,
My lady's sure to wear her sash;
Come the ash before the oak,
My lady's sure to wear her cloak.

ANON

If bees stay at home,
The rain will soon come;
If bees fly away,
It'll be a fine day.

ANON

WEATHER

Whether the weather be fine,
Or whether the weather be not,
Whether the weather be cold,
Or whether the weather be hot,
We'll weather the weather
Whatever the weather,
Whether we like it or not!

ANON

THE FIRST TOOTH

Through the house what busy joy,
Just because the infant boy
Has a tiny tooth to show!
I have got a double row,
All as white, and all as small;
Yet no one cares for mine at all.
He can say but half a word,
Yet that single sound's preferred
To all the words that I can say
In the longest summer day.
He cannot walk, yet if he put
With mimic motion out his foot,
As if he thought he were advancing,
It's prized more than my best dancing.

CHARLES AND MARY LAMB

Poetry for Children, 1809

A CALENDAR

January brings the snow,
Makes our feet and fingers glow.

February brings the rain,
Thaws the frozen lake again.

March brings breezes, loud and shrill,
To stir the dancing daffodil.

April brings the primrose sweet,
Scatters daisies at our feet.

May brings flocks of pretty lambs
Skipping by their fleecy dams.

June brings tulips, lilies, roses,
Fills the children's hands with posies.

Hot July brings cooling showers,
Apricots and gillyflowers.

August brings the sheaves of corn,
Then the harvest home is borne.

Warm September brings the fruit;
Sportsmen then begin to shoot.

Fresh October brings the pheasant;
Then to gather nuts is pleasant.

Dull November brings the blast;
Then the leaves are whirling fast.

Chill December brings the sleet,
Blazing fire, and Christmas treat.

SARA COLERIDGE

Pretty Lessons in Verse for Good Children, 1834

THE CLASSROOM

A was an Archer who shot at a frog

B was a Butcher who kept a bull-dog

C was a Captain all covered with lace

D was a Drummer who played with much grace

E was an Esquire with pride on his brow

F was a Farmer who followed the plough

G was a Gamester who had but ill-luck

H was a Hunter and hunted a buck

I was an Italian who had a white mouse

J was a Joiner and built up a house

K was a King so mighty and grand

L was a Lady who had a white hand

M was a Miser who hoarded up gold

N was a Nobleman gallant and bold

O was an Organ boy who played about town

P was a Parson who wore a black gown

Q was a Queen who was fond of her people

R was a Robin who perched on a steeple

S was a Sailor who spent all he got

T was a Tinker who mended a pot

U was an Usher who loved little boys

V was a Veteran who sold pretty toys

W was a Watchman who guarded the door

X was eXpensive and so became poor

Y was a Youth who did not love school

Z was a Zany who looked a great fool

ANON

THE OWL

There was an old owl who lived in an oak;
The more he heard, the less he spoke.
The less he spoke, the more he heard.
Why aren't we like that wise old bird?

ANON

DR. FOSTER

Doctor Foster is a good man,
He teaches children all he can:
Reading, writing, arithmetic,
And doesn't forget to use his stick.
When he does he makes them dance
Out of England into France,
Out of France into Spain,
Round the world and back again.

ANON

THE CLASSROOM

NATURAL HISTORY

What are little boys made of?
What are little boys made of?
Frogs and snails and puppy-dogs' tails,
And that are little boys made of.

What are little girls made of?
What are little girls made of?
Sugar and spice and all that's nice,
And that are little girls made of.

What are young men made of?
What are young men made of?
Sighs and leers, and crocodile tears
And that are young men made of.

What are young women made of?
What are young women made of?
Ribbons and laces, and sweet pretty faces,
And that are young women made of.

ANON

JACK

That's Jack;
Lay a stick on his back!
What's he done? I cannot say.
We'll find out tomorrow,
And beat him today.

CHARLES HENRY ROSS

Ye Comical Rhymes of Ancient Times,
Dug up into Jokes for Small Folks, 1862

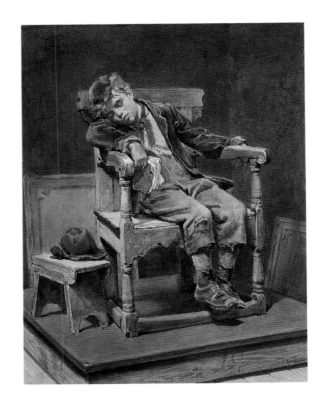

GOOD AND BAD CHILDREN

Children, you are very little,
And your bones are very brittle;
If you would grow great and stately,
You must try to walk sedately.

You must still be bright and quiet,
And content with simple diet;
And remain, through all bewild'ring,
Innocent and honest children.

Happy hearts and happy faces,
Happy play in grassy places –
That was how, in ancient ages,
Children grew to kings and sages.

But the unkind and unruly,
And the sort who eat unduly,
They must never hope for glory –
Theirs is quite a different story!

Cruel children, crying babies,
All grow up as geese and gabies,
Hated, as their age increases,
By their nephews and their nieces.

ROBERT LOUIS STEVENSON,
A Child's Garden of Verses, 1885

COMPARATIVES

Good, better, best,
Never let it rest,
Till your good is better
And your better best.

ANON

A DILLER, A DOLLAR...

A diller, a dollar,
A ten o'clock scholar;
What makes you come so soon?
You used to come at ten o'clock,
But now you come at noon!

ANON

ARITHMETIC

Multiplication is vexation,
Division is as bad;
The Rule of Three it puzzles me,
And fractions drive me mad.

ANON

THREE CHILDREN

Three children sliding on the ice,
All on a summer's day,
And it fell out, they all fell in,
The rest they ran away!

Now, had these children been at home,
Or sliding on dry ground,
Ten thousand pounds to a penny,
They had not all been drowned.

You parents all that children have,
And you that have got none,
If you would have them safe abroad,
Pray keep them safe at home.

TRADITIONAL

HOW TO WRITE A LETTER

Maria intended a letter to write,
But could not begin (as she thought) to indite;
So she went to her mother with pencil and slate,
Containing "Dear Sister," and also a date.

"With nothing to say, my dear girl, do not think
Of wasting your time over paper and ink;
But certainly this is an excellent way,
To try with your slate to find something to say.

"I will give you a rule," said her mother, "my dear,
Just think for a moment your sister is here,
And what would you tell her? Consider, and then
Though silent your tongue, you can speak with your pen."

ELIZABETH TURNER

The Crocus, 1844

TREES

The Oak is called the king of trees,
The Aspen quivers in the breeze,
The Poplar grows up straight and tall,
The Peach tree spreads along the wall,
The Sycamore gives pleasant shade,
The Willow droops in watery glade,
The Fir tree useful timber gives,
The Beech amid the forest lives.

SARA COLERIDGE

Pretty Lessons in Verse for Good Children, 1834

THE STORY OF FIDGETY PHILIP

"Let me see if Philip can
Be a little gentleman;
Let me see if he is able
To sit still for once at table":
Thus Papa bade Phil behave;
And Mama looked very grave.
But fidgety Phil,
He won't sit still;
He wriggles,
And giggles,
And then, I declare,
Swings backwards and forwards,
And tilts up his chair,
Just like any rocking-horse –
"Philip! I am getting cross!"

See the naughty, restless child
Growing still more rude and wild,
Till his chair falls over quite.
Philip screams with all his might,
Catches at the cloth, but then
That makes matters worse again.
Down upon the ground they fall,
Glasses, plates, knives, forks and all.
How Mama did fret and frown,
When she saw them tumbling down!
And Papa made such a face!
Philip is in sad disgrace.

Where is Philip, where is he?
Fairly covered up you see!
Cloth and all are lying on him;
He has pulled down all upon him.
What a terrible to-do!
Dishes, glasses, snapped in two!
Here a knife, and there a fork!
Philip, this is cruel work.
Table all so bare, and ah!
Poor Papa, and poor Mama
Look quite cross, and wonder how
They shall have their dinner now.

HEINRICH HOFFMANN

The English Struwwelpeter
(translator unknown), 1848

LITTLE THINGS

Little drops of water,
　Little grains of sand,
Make the mighty ocean
　And the beauteous land.

And the little moments,
　Humble though they be,
Make the mighty ages
　Of eternity.

So our little errors
   Lead the soul away,
From the paths of virtue
   Into sin to stray.

Little deeds of kindness,
   Little words of love,
Make our earth an Eden,
   Like the heaven above.

JULIA A. CARNEY

Hymns and Sacred Songs, 1855

HISTORY

Willy, Willy, Harry Stee,
Harry, Dick, John, Harry three,
One, two, three, Neds, Richard two,
Henry four, five, six, then who?
Edward four, five, Dick the bad,
Harrys twain and Ned the lad,
Mary, Bessy, James the vain,
Charlie, Charlie, James again!
William and Mary, Ann Gloria,
Four Georges, William – and Victoria!

ANON

THE MONTHS

Thirty days hath September,
April, June and November.
All the rest have thirty-one,
Excepting February alone,
Which has four and twenty-four
Till leap-year gives it one day more.

ANON

HERE LIES FRED

Here lies Fred,
Who was alive and is dead.
Had it been his father,
I had much rather;
Had it been his brother,
Still better than another;
Had it been his sister,
No one would have miss'd her;
Had it been the whole generation,
Still better for the nation;
But since 'tis only Fred,
Who was alive and is dead,
There's no more to be said.

ANON

LOOKING FORWARD

When I am grown to a man's estate
I shall be very proud and great,
And tell the other girls and boys
Not to meddle with my toys.

ROBERT LOUIS STEVENSON

A Child's Garden of Verses, 1885

PLAYTIME

GIRLS AND BOYS COME OUT TO PLAY

Girls and boys, come out to play,
The moon doth shine as bright as day,
Leave your supper and leave your sleep,
And come with your playfellows into the street.
Come with a whoop or come with a call,
Come with a goodwill or not at all.
Up the ladder and down the wall,
A halfpenny roll will serve us all.
You find milk and I'll find flour,
And we'll have a pudding in half an hour!

ANON

One, two, buckle my shoe,
Three, four, shut the door,
Five, six, pick up sticks,
Seven, eight, lay them straight,
Nine, ten, a good fat hen,
Eleven, twelve, who will delve?
Thirteen, fourteen, maids a-courting,
Fifteen, sixteen, maids a-kissing,
Seventeen, eighteen, maids a-waiting,
Nineteen, twenty, my stomach's empty.

ANON

Rub-a-dub-dub,
Three men in a tub,
And how do you think they got there?
The butcher, the baker,
The candlestick-maker,
They all jumped out of a rotten potato,
T'was enough to make a man stare.

ANON

DON'T CARE

Don't-Care – he didn't care,
    Don't-Care was wild:
Don't-Care stole plum and pear
    Like any beggar's child.

Don't-Care was made to care,
    Don't-Care was hung:
Don't-Care was put in a pot
    And stewed till he was done.

ANON

ONE, TWO, THREE, FOUR, FIVE!

One, two, three, four, five!
"Once I caught a fish alive!"
Six, seven, eight, nine, ten!
"Then I let it go again."
"Why did you let it go?"
"Because it bit my finger so."
"Which finger did it bite?"
"This little finger on my right!"

ANON

A GOOD PLAY

We built a ship upon the stair
All made of the back-bedroom chairs,
And filled it full of sofa pillows
To go a-sailing on the billows.

We took a saw and several nails,
And water in the nursery pails;
And Tom said, "Let us also take
An apple and a slice of cake" –
Which was enough for Tom and me
To go a-sailing on, till tea.

We sailed along for days and days,
And had the very best of plays;
But Tom fell out and hurt his knee,
So there was no one left but me.

ROBERT LOUIS STEVENSON
A Child's Garden of Verses, 1885

ST. PAUL'S STEEPLE

Upon Paul's steeple stands a tree,
As full of apples as may be;
The little boys of London town,
They run with hooks to pull them down;
And then they run from hedge to hedge
Until they come to London Bridge.

ANON

Oranges and lemons, say the bells of St. Clement's;
You owe me five farthings, say the bells of St. Martin's;
When will you pay me, say the bells of Old Bailey;
When I grow rich, say the bells of Shoreditch;
When will that be? say the bells of Stepney;
I do not know, says the great bell of Bow.
Here comes a candle to light you to bed,
And here comes a chopper to chop off your head.

ANON

Ride a cock-horse to Banbury Cross,
To see a fine lady upon a white horse;
Rings on her fingers and bells on her toes,
And she shall have music wherever she goes.

ANON

See-saw, Margery Daw,
Johnny shall have a new master;
He shall have but a penny a day,
Because he can't work any faster.

ANON

Cock a doodle doo!
My dame has lost her shoe;
My master's lost his fiddling stick,
And don't know what to do.

Cock a doodle doo!
What is my dame to do?
Till master finds his fiddling stick,
She'll dance without her shoe.

Cock a doodle doo!
My dame has found her shoe,
And master's found his fiddling stick,
Sing doodle doodle doo!

Cock a doodle doo!
My dame will dance with you,
While master fiddles his fiddling stick
For dame and doodle doo.

ANON

TOM, JILL AND BOB

Tom tied a kettle to the tail of a cat,
Jill put a stone in the blind man's hat,
Bob threw his grandmother down the stairs —
And they all grew up ugly, and nobody cares.

ANON

As I was going to sell my eggs,
I met a man with bandy legs,
Bandy legs and crooked toes;
I tripped up his heels, and he fell on his nose.

ANON

As I was walking down the lake,
I met a little rattlesnake,
I gave him so much jelly-cake
It made his little belly ache.
One, two, three, out goes she!

ANON

AGAINST IDLENESS

My mother said
That I never should
Play with the gypsies
In the wood;
If I did she would say,
Naughty girl to disobey.
Your hair shan't curl,
Your shoes shan't shine,
You naughty girl
You shan't be mine.
My father said
That if I did
He'd bang my head
With the teapot lid.

The wood was dark,
The grass was green,
Up comes Sally
With a tambourine;
Alpaca frock,
New scarf-shawl,
White straw bonnet
And a pink parasol.
I went to the river –
No ship to get across,
I paid ten shillings
For an old blind horse;
I up on his back
And off in a crack,
Sally tell my mother
I shall never come back.

ANON

THE MULBERRY BUSH

Here we go round the mulberry bush,
        the mulberry bush,
        the mulberry bush,
Here we go round the mulberry bush,
All on a frosty morning.

This is the way we clap our hands,
This is the way we clap our hands,
This is the way we clap our hands,
All on a frosty morning.

ANON

You, North must go,
To a hut of snow
You, South in a trice,
To an island of spice;
You, off to China,
And sit on a hill!
And you to that chair,
And be five minutes still!

ANON

Ring-a-ring o'roses,
A pocket full of posies,
   A-tishoo! A-tishoo!
We all fall down.

The cows are in the meadow
Lying fast asleep,
   A-tishoo! A-tishoo!
We all get up again.

ANON

WHAT A TO-DO

What a to-do to die today
At a minute or two to two.
A thing distinctly hard to say,
But harder still to do.
For they beat a tattoo at twenty to two
Arrattatatatatatatatatoo
And the dragon will come
When he hears the drum
At a minute or two to two today
At a minute or two to two.

ANON

SUNNY DAYS

THE SKYLARK

The earth was green, the sky was blue:
    I saw and heard one sunny morn
A skylark hang between the two,
    A singing speck above the corn;

A stage below, in gay accord,
    White butterflies danced on the wing,
And still the singing skylark soared,
    And silent sank, and soared to sing.

The cornfield stretched a tender green
    To right and left beside my walks;
I knew he had a nest unseen
    Somewhere among the million stalks.

And as I paused to hear his song,
    While swift the sunny moments slid,
Perhaps his mate sat listening long,
    And listened longer than I did.

CHRISTINA GEORGINA ROSSETTI

Sing-Song, 1872

TUMBLING

In jumping and tumbling
    We spend the whole day,
Till night by arriving
    Has finished our play.

What then? One and all,
    There's no more to be said,
As we tumbled all day,
    So we tumble to bed.

ANON

I REMEMBER, I REMEMBER

I remember, I remember
The house where I was born,
The little window where the sun
Came peeping in at morn;
He never came a wink too soon
Nor brought too long a day;
But now, I often wish the night
Had borne my breath away.

I remember, I remember
The roses, red and white,
The violets and the lily-cups –
Those flowers made of light!
The lilacs where the robin built,
And where my brother set
The laburnum on his birthday, –
The tree is living yet!

I remember, I remember
Where I was used to swing,
And thought the air must rush as fresh
To swallows on the wing;
My spirit flew in feathers then
That is so heavy now,
The summer pools could hardly cool
The fever on my brow.

I remember, I remember
The fir-trees dark and high;
I used to think their slender tops
Were close against the sky:
It was a childish ignorance,
But now 'tis little joy
To know I'm farther off from Heaven
Than when I was a boy.

THOMAS HOOD

The Plea of the Midsummer Fairies, 1827

THE SWALLOW

Fly away, fly away, over the sea,
Sun-loving swallow, for summer is done.
Come again, come again, come back to me,
Bringing the summer and bringing the sun.

CHRISTINA GEORGINA ROSSETTI

Sing-Song, 1872

Sukey, you shall be my wife,
And I will tell you why:
I have got a little pig,
And you have got a sty;
I have got a dun cow,
And you can make good cheese;
Sukey, will you have me?
Say "yes," if you please.

ANON

A PROPOSAL

Bonny lass, pretty lass, wilt thou be mine?
Thou shalt not wash dishes,
Nor yet serve the swine;
Thou shalt sit on a cushion and sew a fine seam,
And thou shalt eat strawberries, sugar and cream!

TRADITIONAL

WHAT IS PINK?

What is pink? A rose is pink
By the fountain's brink.
What is red? A poppy's red
In its barley bed.
What is blue? The sky is blue
Where the clouds float through.
What is white? A swan is white
Sailing in the light.
What is yellow? Pears are yellow,
Rich and ripe and mellow.

What is green? The grass is green,
With small flowers between.
What is violet? Clouds are violet
In the summer twilight.
What is orange? Why, an orange,
Just an orange!

CHRISTINA GEORGINA ROSSETTI

Sing-Song, 1872

PIRATE STORY

Three of us afloat in the meadow by the swing,
 Three of us aboard in the basket on the lea.
Winds are in the air, they are blowing in the spring;
 And waves are on the meadow like the waves there are at sea.

Where shall we adventure, to-day that we're afloat.
 Wary of the weather and steering by a star?
Shall it be to Africa, a-steering of the boat,
 To Providence, or Babylon, or off to Malabar?

Hi! but here's a squadron a-rowing on the sea —
 Cattle on the meadow a-charging with a roar!
Quick, and we'll escape them, they're as mad as they can be,
 The wicket is the harbour and the garden is the shore.

ROBERT LOUIS STEVENSON
A Child's Garden of Verses, 1885

THE RIVER'S SONG

Clear and cool, clear and cool,
By laughing shallow, and dreaming pool;
Cool and clear, cool and clear,
By shining shingle, and foaming weir;
Under the crag where the ouzel sings,
And the ivied wall where the church-bell rings,
Undefiled, for the undefiled;
Play by me, bathe in me, mother and child.

Dank and foul, dank and foul,
By the smoky town in its murky cowl;
Foul and dank, foul and dank,
By wharf and sewer and slimy bank;
Darker and darker the further I go,
Baser and baser the richer I grow;
Who dare sport with the sin-defiled?
Shrink from me, turn from me, mother and child.

Strong and free, strong and free,
The floodgates are open, away to the sea.
Free and strong, free and strong,
Cleansing my streams as I hurry along,
To the golden sands, and the leaping bar,
And the taintless tide that awaits me afar,
As I lose myself in the infinite main,
Like a soul that has sinned and is pardoned again.
Undefiled, for the undefiled;
Play by me, bathe in me, mother and child.

CHARLES KINGSLEY

The Water Babies, 1863

THE RAINBOW

Boats sail on the rivers,
    And ships sail on the seas;
But clouds that sail across the sky
    Are prettier far than these.

There are bridges on the rivers,
    As pretty as you please;
But the bow that bridges heaven,
    And overtops the trees,
And builds a road from earth to sky,
    Is prettier far than these.

CHRISTINA GEORGINA ROSSETTI

Sing-Song, 1872

BED IN SUMMER

In winter I get up at night
And dress by yellow candle-light.
In summer quite the other way,
I have to go to bed by day.

I have to go to bed and see
The birds still hopping on the tree,
Or hear the grown-up people's feet
Still going past me in the street.

And does it not seem hard to you,
When all the sky is clear and blue,
And I should like so much to play,
To have to go to bed by day?

ROBERT LOUIS STEVENSON

A Child's Garden of Verses, 1885

DOWN IN YONDER MEADOW

Down in yonder meadow where the green grass
grows,
Pretty Pollie Pillicote bleaches her clothes.
She sang, she sang, she sang, oh, so sweet,
She sang, *Oh, come over!* across the street.

He kissed her, he kissed her, he bought her a gown,

He bought her a gown and a guinea gold ring,
A guinea, a guinea, a guinea gold ring.

Up street, and down, shine the windows made of glass,
Oh, isn't Pollie Pillicote a braw young lass?
Cherries in her cheeks and ringlets in her hair,
Hear her singing *Handy Dandy* up and down the stair.

ANON

Lavender's blue, dilly, dilly,
Lavender's green.
When I am king, dilly, dilly,
You shall be queen.
Who told you so, dilly, dilly,
Who told you so?
'Twas mine own heart, dilly, dilly
That told me so.

Call up your men, dilly, dilly,
Set them to work,
Some with a rake, dilly, dilly,
Some with a fork.
Some to make hay, dilly, dilly,
Some to thresh corn,
Whilst you and I, dilly, dilly,
Keep ourselves warm.

ANON

IF NO ONE EVER MARRIES ME

If no one ever marries me —
And I don't see why they should,
For nurse says I'm not pretty,
And I'm seldom very good —

If no one ever marries me
I shan't mind very much,
I shall buy a squirrel in a cage
And a little rabbit-hutch;

I shall have a cottage near a wood,
And a pony all my own
And a little lamb, quite clean and tame,
That I can take to town.

And when I'm getting really old —
At twenty-eight or nine —
I shall buy a little orphan-girl
And bring her up as mine.

LAURENCE ALMA-TADEMA

Realm of Unknown Kings, 1897

THE CITY CHILD

Dainty little maiden, whither would you wander?
Whither from this pretty home, the home where mother dwells?
"Far and far away," said the dainty little maiden,
"All among the gardens, aurioulas, anemones,
Roses and lilies and Canterbury-bells."

Dainty little maiden, whither would you wander?
Whither from this pretty house, this city-house of ours?
"Far and far away," said the dainty little maiden,
"All among the meadows, the clover and the clematis,
Daisies and kingcups and honeysuckle flowers."

ALFRED, LORD TENNYSON

Sea Dreams and Idylls, 1860

THE MERMAID

Who would be
A mermaid fair,
Singing alone,
Combing her hair
Under the sea,
In a golden curl
With a comb of pearl,
On a throne?

I would be a mermaid fair;
I would sing to myself the whole of the day.
With a comb of pearl I would comb my hair;
And still as I combed I would sing and say,
"Who is it loves me? who loves not me?"
I would comb my hair till my ringlets would fall,
        Low adown, low adown,
And I should look like a fountain of gold
        Singing alone
        With a shrill inner sound,
        Over the throne
        In the midst of the hall.

ALFRED, LORD TENNYSON

Poems Chiefly Lyrical, 1830

CATKIN

I have a little pussy
And her coat is silver-grey;
She lives in a great wide meadow
And she never runs away.
She'll always be a pussy,
She'll never be a cat,
Because – she's a pussy willow!
Now what do you think of that?

ANON

The man in the wilderness asked of me,
How many strawberries grow in the sea?
I answered him as I thought good,
As many red herrings as grow in the wood.

ANON

Mirror, mirror, tell me,
Am I pretty or plain?
Or am I downright ugly
And ugly to remain?
Shall I marry a gentleman?
Shall I marry a clown?
Or shall I marry old Knives and Scissors
A-shouting through the town?

ANON

THE POETS

ALMA-TADEMA, Laurence
(1865–1940) UK
Daughter of the pre-Raphaelite painter Sir
Lawrence Alma-Tadema. A close friend of
the pianist and politician Paderewski. She
died a spinster, as she had prophesied.

CARNEY, Julia A. (1823–1908) USA
A schoolteacher from Boston. It is said that
she improvised "Little Things" as an
edifying tract while teaching class one day
in 1845.

COLERIDGE, Sara (1802–1852) UK
The daughter of Samuel Taylor Coleridge.
Brought up in the company of Southey and
Wordsworth near Keswick in England's
Lake District, in 1829 she married her
cousin Henry Coleridge and moved to
London. Aside from *Pretty Lessons in Verse
for Good Children* (1834), and a fairy story,
Phantasmion (1837), she produced no
original work, but devoted herself to editing
and annotating her father's works. It is
widely believed that she thus denied the
world one of its most sensitive and
intelligent poets.

HARDY, Thomas (1840–1928) UK
Poet and novelist. Initially an architect,
Hardy wrote a large number of very
popular novels about his native Dorset,
including *Tess of the d'Urbervilles* (1891) and
Jude the Obscure (1895). He regarded fiction,
however, merely as a means of making a
living, and longed instead to write verse.
After the publication of *Jude the Obscure* he
gave up novel writing and devoted the rest
of his life to poetry. Although they use
conventional forms, Hardy's poems are
startlingly original in tone and in syntax.

HOFFMANN, Heinrich (1809–1894)
Germany
A Frankfurt doctor, Hoffmann worked in
an asylum. He wrote and illustrated
Struwwelpeter as a moral lesson book that
would not frighten its readers.

HOOD, Thomas (1799–1845) UK
Born in London, the son of a Scottish
bookseller and printer, Hood contributed to
magazines and studied engraving before
appointment as sub-editor on the *London
Magazine,* where he met de Quincey, Lamb,
and others. The great parodist John
Hamilton Reynolds became Hood's closest
friend and collaborator, and Hood married
his sister. He edited several magazines and
his works achieved considerable popularity,
notably the *Song of the Shirt* (1843) and the
Bridge of Sighs (1843), which combine the
faint tone of pathos so characteristic of
Hood's work and the jaunty humour which,
according to his friends, he always evinced.

KINGSLEY, Charles (1819–1875) UK
Born in England at Holne, Dartmoor,
Kingsley became rector of Eversley in
Hampshire (1844) after a Cambridge
education. A novelist, journalist, and
historian, he was Professor of Modern
History at Cambridge from 1860 to 1869.

LAMB, Charles (1775–1834) and Mary
(1764–1847) UK
Although a humorous and gentle man,
Charles Lamb was haunted by fear of
hereditary madness. His elder sister, Mary,
murdered their mother in 1796, after which
he took Mary into his care. His best known
work is contained in the *Essays of Elia*
(1823). Charles and Mary were coauthors of
Tales from Shakespeare (1807), an attempt to
render Shakespeare's plots accessible to
children. Charles's famous poem "On an
Infant Dying as Soon as Born" (1827),
concerns the baby son of his friend and
collaborator Thomas Hood (q.v.).

ROSS, Charles Henry (1841–1897) UK
At first Ross was a clerk at the British
Public Records Office at Somerset House
in London, and then a cartoonist, editor of
Judy, a rhymester, and author.

ROSSETTI, Christina Georgina
(1830–1894) UK
Sister of the poet and painter Dante
Gabriel Rossetti, Christina led a sad life
and failed to fulfill her early exceptional
promise. She twice rejected suitors because
of her high Anglican religious principles,

and her verses are devout and full of the sadness of "what might have been". Her first collection, *Goblin Market* (1862), was very much her finest, but *Sing-Song* (1872) is full of charming, simple verses for children. She was always frail and, at the time of *Sing-Song's* composition, was very close to death from Grave's disease. Thereafter, she taught with her mother and wrote morally improving verse.

STEVENSON, Robert Louis (1850–1894) UK
A master stylist and supremely imaginative writer who contrived to lead a hero's life despite often crippling illness. All his life he suffered from chronic bronchial problems and acute nervous excitability. Stevenson nonetheless travelled extensively, wrote many fine essays and novels and in *A Child's Garden of Verses* (1885) applied his highly developed gifts of imagination and sympathy to the emotions and enthusiasms of childhood. In so doing he can be said to have invented a whole new genre of verse. In 1888 he travelled in the South Seas and at last settled with his family in Samoa where the natives called him "Tusitala" (the tale-teller). He died there of a brain haemorrhage. His novels include *Treasure Island* (1883), *Kidnapped* (1886), *Catriona* (1893), and, for older readers, the eerie *Strange Case of Dr. Jekyll and Mr. Hyde* (1886).

TENNYSON, Alfred Lord (1809–1892) UK
Although the most honoured and fêted poet of the Victorian era, Tennyson liked to live "far from the madding crowd" in Hampshire or on the Isle of Wight. He was very prolific and, although he never wrote specifically for children, many of his works have become firm favourites with young people because of their grand romantic subject matter or because they are ideal for reciting.

TURNER, Elizabeth (1775–1846) UK
A popular children's poet, Elizabeth Turner lived at Whitchurch in Shropshire. All her books had the names of flowers: "The Daisy" (1807), "The Cowslip" (1811), "The Pink" (1823), and "The Bluebell" (1838).

WORDSWORTH, William (1770–1850) UK
Poet Laureate. He lived at Grasmere in the English Lake District with his sister Dorothy. At his best, as in "The Prelude" or "Tintern Abbey", Wordsworth was a brilliant, thoughtful nature poet; at his worst he was capable of gaucheness and banality.

THE PAINTERS

A BRIEF NOTE ON SOME OF THE ANONYMOUS VERSES

The age of some familiar rhymes is consistently surprising. "Multiplication is Vexation" is first found in a manuscript of 1570. "Thirty Days hath September" is quoted in *Return From Parnassus,* a drama of 1606, while "A Swarm of Bees in May" is, at the least, three hundred years old, as is "Ride a Cock-Horse" (Banbury Cross – one of the *"chere reine"* crosses – was demolished in the seventeenth century). An early variant of "Three Children Sliding on the Ice" dates back to 1662.

INDEX OF FIRST LINES

Other Premier Picturemacs you will enjoy

A FIRST TREASURY OF FAIRY TALES Edited by Michael Foss
A SECOND TREASURY OF FAIRY TALES Edited by Michael Foss
THE MAGIC OINTMENT Eric Quayle/Michael Foreman
BLACK BEAUTY Anna Sewell/Robin McKinley/Susan Jeffers
THE ENCHANTER'S SPELL Illustrated by Gennady Spirin
THE ENCHANTED WORLD Part One Amabel Williams-Ellis/Moira Kemp
THE ENCHANTED WORLD Part Two Amabel Williams-Ellis/Moira Kemp

For a complete list of Picturemac and Premier Picturemac
titles write to:

Macmillan Children's Books,
18–21 Cavaye Place, London SW10 9PG